Contents

A **pull-out answers section** (pages A1 to A8) appears in the centre of this book, between pages 20 and 21. It also gives simple guidance on how best to use this book. Remove this section before you begin working through the tests.

Target time: 12 minutes

Underline the two words, **one** from each group, that mean almost the **same**.

> **Example** (typical, <u>false</u>, halt)   (unusual, real, <u>untrue</u>)

1. (tired, grumpy, cheerful)   (sad, joyful, tried)
2. (rain, cloud, damp)   (dry, wet, towel)
3. (win, beat, team)   (hit, ball, hurt)

Choose the word that best completes the sentence. Underline the answer.

> **Example** **Music** is to **listen** as **food** is to (touch, <u>taste</u>, drop).

4. **Sleep** is to **bedroom** as **cook** is to (eat, kitchen, stir).
5. **School** is to **teacher** as **hospital** is to (sick, doctor, ambulance).
6. **Cat** is to **meow** as **dog** is to (bark, quack, hoot).

Underline the two words, **one** from each group, that are most **opposite** in meaning.

> **Example** (<u>after</u>, morning, begin)   (<u>before</u>, then, when)

7. (write, right, lift)   (left, draw, carry)
8. (cat, chair, sit)   (fell, stand, bend)
9. (wash, clean, bob)   (dirty, fork, sink)

Underline the word that goes best with the three words in brackets.

> **Example** (wet, soaking, moist)   <u>damp</u>, swamp, rotten

10. (yellow, pink, blue)   green, sun, read
11. (van, lorry, truck)   road, lady, car
12. (mouse, frog, bird)   person, kangaroo, zoo

End of test

Score:		Time taken:		Target met?	

Target time: **12 minutes**

1–3. For each of the words below, choose the correct group. Write its letter on the line.

F = fish **B** = bird

robin _____   tuna _____   cuckoo _____

owl _____   trout _____   cod _____

In each group, three words go together and one is the odd one out. Underline the word that does **not** go with the other three.

Example pound   <u>coin</u>   hit   thump

4. door   road   window   floor
5. field   branch   twig   leaf
6. car   lorry   driver   van

Underline the pair of words that are most **opposite** in meaning.

Example (begin, when)   (morning, then)   <u>(after, before)</u>

7. (race, sprint)   (jog, cross)   (quick, slow)
8. (rich, poor)   (paw, money)   (coin, spend)
9. (come, go)   (start, leaf)   (house, room)

Two words in each sentence must change places so that the sentence makes sense. Underline the two words.

Example I <u>a need nap</u>.   (I <u>need a</u> nap.)

10. The train fast is.
11. How many boats can see you?
12. My cat likes to milk drink.

End of test.

Score:		Time taken:		Target met?	

Section 1 Test 3

■ Underline the pair of words that mean almost the **same**.

> **Example** (typical, unusual) (halt, real) (<u>false, untrue</u>)

1. (smart, clever) (glass, plate) (shiny, silly)

2. (hug, give) (wind, story) (finish, end)

3. (hungry, eat) (drip, fat) (slim, thin)

■ Choose the word that best completes the sentence. Underline the answer.

> **Example** **Music** is to **listen** as **food** is to (touch, <u>taste</u>, drop).

4. **Right** is to **left** as **fast** is to (quick, rapid, slow).

5. **Yes** is to **no** as **wrong** is to (right, left, behind).

6. **Cat** is to **kitten** as **dog** is to (puppy, foal, lamb).

■ 7–9. Look at these groups. For each of the words below, choose the correct group. Write its letter on the line.

A	B
lion	cow
tiger	sheep

giraffe _____   duck _____   leopard _____

pig _____   elephant _____   goat _____

■ In each group, three words go together and one is the odd one out. Underline the word that does **not** go with the other three.

> **Example** pound   <u>coin</u>   hit   thump

10. petal   chair   leaf   stem

11. lion   tiger   leopard   giraffe

12. shiny   dirty   spotless   clean

End of test.

Score:		Time taken:		Target met?	

Target time: **12 minutes**

Find the missing number in each equation. Write it on the line.

> **Example** 3 + 3 = 4 + ___2___   (3 + 3 = 6 and so does 4 + 2)

1. 100 ÷ 10 = 19 – _____

2. 7 × 10 = 60 + _____

3. 27 – 5 = 12 + _____

4. 14 + 9 = 29 – _____

Match the number codes to the words. Use this to help you work out the answers to the questions. Write your answers on the lines.

> JAW   PAW   JAR   917   615   617

5. What is the code for **WAR**? _____

6. What is the code for **WRAP**? _____

7. What does the code **1615** mean? _____

Underline the pair of words that are most **opposite** in meaning.

> **Example** (begin, when)   (morning, then)   (after, before)

8. (foot, slipper)   (run, walk)   (bend, lean)

9. (funny, film)   (dip, hop)   (laugh, cry)

10. (plate, dinner)   (glass, trip)   (break, fix)

11. (stay, leave)   (step, wait)   (holiday, home)

Circle the letter next to the **true** statement.

12. People use telephones to talk to other people. Ed is using a telephone.

If the above statements are true, which one of the following statements must also be true?
A. Ed is ordering a pizza.
B. Ed cannot hear the person he is talking to.
C. Ed is talking to somebody.
D. Ed will be using the telephone for a long time.

End of test.

Score:		Time taken:		Target met?	

Schofield & Sims

the long-established educational publisher specialising in maths, English and science

Verbal Reasoning 2 is a collection of short, language-based problem solving tests. Each timed test includes age-appropriate questions, providing opportunities for children to practise and master verbal reasoning skills in preparation for the 11+ and other school selection tests. This book is part of the **Rapid Reasoning Tests** series and covers the following question types: word and letter patterns; vocabulary; spelling; number patterns and problem solving.

Rapid Reasoning Tests provides short, effective, timed tests in reasoning. The series comprises six books of verbal reasoning tests and six books of non-verbal reasoning tests.

Written by experienced teachers and designed for independent use, **Rapid Reasoning Tests** has been carefully structured to provide practice of key, standard format question types. Each collection of tests has been designed for use over one year and provides one section per term in order to support regular practice.

Key features

- **Short tests** requiring few resources that are easy to fit into a busy timetable.
- A **target time** for each test encourages children to work quickly and develop the necessary exam skills for success in the 11+ and other tests.
- **Pull-out answers** in the centre of each book can be easily removed.
- **Free downloads** to support the series are available from the Schofield & Sims website.

The full series includes the following books:

Verbal Reasoning 1 978 07217 1238 3	**Non-verbal Reasoning 1** 978 07217 1226 0	**(Ages 6–7)**
Verbal Reasoning 2 978 07217 1239 0	**Non-verbal Reasoning 2** 978 07217 1227 7	**(Ages 7–8)**
Verbal Reasoning 3 978 07217 1240 6	**Non-verbal Reasoning 3** 978 07217 1228 4	**(Ages 8–9)**
Verbal Reasoning 4 978 07217 1241 3	**Non-verbal Reasoning 4** 978 07217 1229 1	**(Ages 9–10)**
Verbal Reasoning 5 978 07217 1242 0	**Non-verbal Reasoning 5** 978 07217 1230 7	**(Ages 10–11)**
Verbal Reasoning 6 978 07217 1243 7	**Non-verbal Reasoning 6** 978 07217 1231 4	**(Ages 11–12)**

FSC MIX Paper from responsible sources FSC® C110589

ISBN 978 07217 1239 0
Key Stage 2
Age range 7–8
£3.95
(Retail price)

ISBN 978-07217-1239-0

9 780721 712390

For further information and to place an order visit
www.schofieldandsims.co.uk or telephone 01484 607080

Target time: **12 minutes**

■ Take a letter away from each word to make two new words. The letter you take away should be in the same position in each word in the pair.

Example chat, flan _____cat_____ , _____fan_____ (remove the second letter from each word)

1. tall, till _____ , _____

2. wink, tank _____ , _____

3. gate, sown _____ , _____

■ In each of the sentences below, the word in capitals has three letters missing. Those three letters spell a word. Write the three-letter word in the gap.

Example My favourite toy is my teddy B E A R . (EAR)

4. That is a pretty G __ __ __ ring.

5. The zebra has black and white S T __ __ __ E S .

6. The cat caught some M __ __ __ .

■ If these words were listed in alphabetical order, which word would come **first**? Write the answer on the line.

Example water milk juice cup jug _____cup_____

7. table chair paper pencil floor _____

8. fruit cheese cracker milk bread _____

9. cat mouse bird fish dog _____

■ Find the missing letter that completes **both** words. Write the letter on the line. Choose your answer from these letters:

d m g e p

Example bea (m) atch (beam and match)

10. soun (__) ance

11. dam (__) lane

12. goin (__) loat

End of test.

Score:		Time taken:		Target met?	

Find the **three-letter word** hidden in each longer word. You will not need to change the letter order. Underline the word and write it on the line.

Example st<u>oo</u>p _____too_____

1. alarm _____

2. float _____

3. women _____

Find the missing letter that completes **both** words. Write the letter on the line. Choose your answer from these letters:

l n h t d m

Example bea (_m_) atch   (beam and match)

4. trai (__) ift

5. fres (__) aunt

6. trea (__) each

Underline the **two** words that contain all the same letters.

Example sip   <u>asp</u>   pit   <u>sap</u>   sit

7. tip   not   ton   toe   nut

8. pan   pun   nip   nap   pot

9. nab   net   nip   tom   ten

Underline the two words, **one** from each group, that together make one new word. The word from the first group comes first.

Example (<u>bas</u>ket, bag, shop)   (pin, <u>ball</u>, bin)   (basketball)

10. (garden, house, pot)   (hold, flower, traffic)

11. (step, walk, roof)   (tiles, road, ladder)

12. (deaf, blind, old)   (young, fold, sound)

End of test.

Score:		Time taken:		Target met?	

Target time: 12 minutes

Change the first word into the last word. Only change one letter at a time. You must make a new word in the middle. Write the new word on the line.

Example SIN [____BIN____] BIG

1. SUN [_____] BUG
2. LOG [_____] DON
3. BUN [_____] CUT

In each of the sentences below, the word in capitals has three letters missing. Those three letters spell a word. Write the three-letter word in the gap.

Example My favourite toy is my teddy B E A R.   (EAR)

4. I have a pencil and a __ __ __ BER but no pen.

5. I have visited my FRI __ __ __ .

6. On a sunny day I enjoy a cold DR __ __ __ .

Underline the two words, **one** from each group, that together make one new word. The word from the first group comes first.

Example (basket, bag, shop)   (pin, ball, bin)   (basketball)

7. (nails, tooth, fingers)   (glove, clipper, paste)

8. (teeth, skin, hair)   (shampoo, brush, wash)

9. (light, bright, yellow)   (lamp, shed, house)

If these words were listed in alphabetical order, which word would come **last**? Write the answer on the line.

Example water milk juice cup jug   ___water___

10. five   four   six   two   eight   _____

11. silly   flower   climb   string   great   _____

12. nail   hammer   spanner   screw   drill   _____

End of test.

Score:	Time taken:	Target met?

Find the next number in the sequence. Write it on the line.

> **Example** 18   16   14   12   10   ___8___   (–2 each time)

1. 3   6   9   12   15   _____

2. 75   65   55   45   35   _____

3. 4   8   12   16   20   _____

Use the information given to answer the sum. Write your answer as a **letter**.

> **Example** A = 2   B = 4   C = 5   D = 6   **A + B =** ___D___   (2 + 4 = 6)

4. A = 9   B = 6   C = 8   D = 2   **D + B =** _____

5. A = 3   B = 5   C = 4   D = 7   **A + C =** _____

6. A = 1   B = 9   C = 10   D = 20   **C – B =** _____

Work out the missing number. Write it on the line.

> **Example** 5 [9] 4   2 [5] 3   7 [___10___] 3
> (a + b = ?, where a is the number on the left and b is the number on the right)

7. 2 [11] 9   26 [30] 4   5 [_____] 17

8. 20 [37] 17   112 [112] 0   19 [_____] 31

9. 13 [15] 2   50 [89] 39   3 [_____] 12

Find the missing number in each equation. Write it on the line.

> **Example** 3 + 3 = 4 + ___2___   (3 + 3 = 6 and so does 4 + 2)

10. 10 ÷ 2 = 3 + _____

11. 2 × 6 = 13 – _____

12. 2 × 2 = 1 + _____

End of test.

Score:		Time taken:		Target met?	

Target time: **12 minutes**

■ Find the next letter pair in the sequence. Use the alphabet to help you. Write your answer on the line.

A B C D E F G H I J K L M N O P Q R S T U V W X Y Z

Example AB   BC   CD   DE   EF   _FG_   (+1, +1)

1. AA   BB   CC   DD   _____

2. LL   MM   NN   OO   _____

3. RR   SS   TT   UU   _____

■ Find the letter that completes each sentence. Use the alphabet to help you. Write your answer on the line.

A B C D E F G H I J K L M N O P Q R S T U V W X Y Z

Example **C** is to **D** as **E** is to ___F___ .   (+1)

4. **X** is to **Z** as **M** is to _____ .   5. **E** is to **H** as **Q** is to _____ .   6. **W** is to **U** as **L** is to _____ .

■ Make a new word. Change the third pair of words in the same way as the other pairs. Write the new word on the line.

Example (bank, ban)   (cool, coo)   (dent, ___den___)
(take away the last letter of the first word)

7. (down, don)   (cold, cod)   (long, _____)

8. (trap, tap)   (clog, cog)   (pain, _____)

9. (four, our)   (down, own)   (fold, _____)

■ Match the number codes to the words. Use this to help you work out the answers to the questions. Write your answers on the lines.

CAT   TOY   COT   831   851   156

10. What is the code for **COT**? _____

11. What is the code for **TOY**? _____

12. What does the code **831** mean? _____

End of test.

Score:		Time taken:		Target met?	

Target time: **12 minutes**

 Work out the missing number. Write it on the line.

Example 5 [9] 4   2 [5] 3   7 [__10__] 3

(a + b = ?, where a is the number on the left and b is the number on the right)

1. 75 [100] 25   53 [76] 23   1 [_____] 72

2. 11 [6] 5   27 [20] 7   6 [_____] 0

3. 20 [8] 12   34 [11] 23   56 [_____] 49

Find the missing number in each equation. Write it on the line.

Example 3 + 3 = 4 + __2__   (3 + 3 = 6 and so does 4 + 2)

4. 14 + 6 = 2 × _____

5. 70 ÷ 10 = 4 + _____

6. 11 × 5 = 1 + _____

Find the next number in the sequence. Write it on the line.

Example 18   16   14   12   10   __8__   (–2 each time)

7. 4   8   12   16   _____

8. 13   24   35   46   _____

9. 10   15   20   25   _____

Use the information given to answer the sum. Write your answer as a **letter**.

Example A = 2   B = 4   C = 5   D = 6   **A + B =** __D__   (2 + 4 = 6)

10. A = 3   B = 3   C = 9   D = 6   **D + B =** _____

11. A = 7   B = 11   C = 5   D = 4   **B – D =** _____

12. A = 10   B = 2   C = 12   D = 6   **B × D =** _____

End of test

Score:		Time taken:		Target met?	

Target time: **12 minutes**

■ Find the code. Use the alphabet to help you. Write your answer on the line.

A B C D E F G H I J K L M N O P Q R S T U V W X Y Z

Example If the code for **FIT** is **GJU**, what does **XBE** mean? ___WAD___

(–1 from the code to the word)

1. If the code **BSN** means **ARM**, what does the code **UPQ** mean? _____

2. If the code **BHF** means **AGE**, what does the code **BJN** mean? _____

3. If **ALL** is written in code as **DOO**, what does the code **PXG** mean? _____

■ Match the number codes to the words. Use this to help you work out the answers to the questions. Write your answers on the lines.

PIP   PIG   GET   356   672   353

4. What is the code for **PEG**? _____

5. What is the code for **PIT**? _____

6. What does the code **3537** mean? _____

■ The word in the square brackets has been made by some of the letters from the two outside words. Make a new word in the middle of the second group of words in the same way. Write the new word on the line.

Example (left [lead] read)   (jogs [___joke___] pike)

7. (rain [into] toll)   (soon [_____] cent)

8. (both [boat] heat)   (nice [_____] bone)

9. (real [read] aids)   (tuck [_____] neat)

■ Find the next letter pair in the sequence. Use the alphabet to help you. Write your answer on the line.

A B C D E F G H I J K L M N O P Q R S T U V W X Y Z

Example AB BC CD DE EF ___FG___   (+1, +1)

10. PP QQ PP QQ _____

11. AZ BY CX DW _____

12. FG GH HI IJ _____

End of test.

Score:	Time taken:	Target met?

■ Read the following information. Work out the answers. Write your answers on the lines.

1. My father is writing letters. He writes to his father before he writes to his sister. He writes to his mother first. Who does he write to third? _____

2. A group of children are asked to line up to enter the classroom. Mary is first in the line. James is two places behind her. Shazia is second in the line. Who is third in the line? _____

3. Phil is 17 and his brother is 23. Phil's father is 25 years older than Phil.
   How old is Phil's father? _____

4. Charlotte takes her dog for 2 walks every day. On how many walks does Charlotte take her dog in 1 week? _____

■ Choose the correct statement for each question. Circle the letter next to the **true** statement.

5. Supermarkets sell food. People go shopping in supermarkets.

   If the above statements are true, which one of the following statements must also be true?
   A. People listen to music in supermarkets.
   B. Newspapers are sold in supermarkets.
   C. Supermarkets are very noisy places.
   D. People can buy food in supermarkets.

6. Birds eat berries and insects. A robin is a type of bird.

   If the above statements are true, which one of the following statements must also be true?
   A. Robins eat insects and berries.
   B. Robins can be seen in the garden.
   C. Birds build their nests in hedges.
   D. Robins like hopping around in the snow.

■ Read the following questions. Work out the answers. Write your answers on the lines.

7. What is the day before Friday? _____

8. Which is the first month of the year in the UK? _____

9. If today is Friday, what day will it be tomorrow? _____

10. If it is October now, which month comes next? _____

11. My brother is 2 years older than me. I am 5. How old is my brother? _____

12. In which season is the weather coldest? _____

End of test.

Score:		Time taken:		Target met?	

Target time: **12 minutes**

■ Read the following information. Work out the answers. Write your answers on the lines.

1. Three baby birds called Peep, Cheep and Tweet are learning to fly. Cheep jumps out of the tree first. Tweet jumps out after Cheep and Peep.
Who is the second bird to jump? _____

2. Ajay is delivering newspapers to houses A, B and C. He goes to house B third and house C first.
Which house does Ajay visit second? _____

3. It is midday now.
What time was it **3** hours ago? _____

4. Billy has **19** stickers. **3** are blue, **8** are pink and **2** are green. The rest are purple.
How many purple stickers does Billy have? _____

5. Jamie is posting letters. He posts **2** at house A, **3** at house B and **4** at house E.
How many letters does Jamie deliver altogether? _____

6. Katie has **3** pink jumpers, **2** green hats, **4** blue pairs of trousers and **4** pink t-shirts.
How many pink pieces of clothing does Katie have? _____

7. Sabine goes for a walk at **3.00** p.m. She gets back from her walk at **4.00** p.m.
How long did Jane's walk last? _____

8. It is **1.00** p.m. now. A television show I want to watch is starting in half an hour.
What time does the television show start? _____

9. It is **5.00** p.m.
What time was it **2** hours ago? _____

10. What time will it be in half an hour if it is **10.30** a.m. now? _____

11. Alan starts his homework at **7.00** p.m. He finishes at **8.00** p.m.
How long did it take Alan to do his homework? _____

12. An hour ago it was **4.00** p.m.
What time is it now? _____

End of test.

Score:		Time taken:		Target met?	

⬇ ■ Read the following information. Work out the answers. Write your answers on the lines.

1. Two girls are sharing some sweets. Becky eats **3** strawberry sweets and **2** lemon sweets. Paula eats **3** lemon sweets and a raspberry sweet. How many lemon sweets did the girls eat between them? _____

2. Aaqib is drawing **10** flowers. He colours **3** flowers pink, **2** yellow and the rest he colours purple. How many purple flowers does Aaqib draw? _____

3. A house has **6** rooms. One is a bathroom, one is a kitchen and the rest are bedrooms. How many bedrooms does the house have? _____

■ Circle the letter next to the **true** statement for each question.

4. Puppets are toys with strings attached to them. Punch and Judy are puppets.

   If the above statements are true, which one of the following statements must also be true?
   A. Punch is very naughty.
   B. Judy's dog steals sausages.
   C. Punch and Judy are real.
   D. Punch and Judy have strings attached to them.

5. Film stars are actors in films. Dev is a famous film star.

   If the above statements are true, which one of the following statements must also be true?
   A. People go to the theatre to see plays.
   B. Dev teaches drama in a school.
   C. Cinemas show popular films.
   D. Dev is an actor.

6. A person who writes stories is called an author. Alice writes lots of stories.

   If the above statements are true, which one of the following statements must also be true?
   A. Alice's sister likes her stories.
   B. Alice is an author.
   C. Alice writes stories on a computer.
   D. Stories are all true.

■ Read the following questions. Work out the answers. Write your answers on the lines.

7. Which day comes after Tuesday? _____

8. Which month comes after January? _____

9. Which day comes before Sunday? _____

10. Sam's friend's birthday is in July. Sam's birthday is **2** months later. When is Sam's birthday? _____

11. If today is Wednesday, what day was it yesterday? _____

12. If it is spring now, which season comes next? _____

End of test.

Score:		Time taken:		Target met?	

Target time: 12 minutes

■ Underline the word in brackets that is **closest** in meaning to the word in capitals.

> **Example** FALSE (real, <u>untrue</u>, halt, typical, unusual)

1. PRESENT (cake, friend, gift, party, wrap)
2. RUSH (stay, leave, rest, hurry, wait)
3. HELP (teach, learn, stuck, aid, fold)
4. START (race, begin, track, lean, car)

■ Choose the word that best completes the sentence. Underline the answer.

> **Example** **Music** is to **listen** as **food** is to (touch, <u>taste</u>, drop).

5. **In** is to **out** as **happy** is to (cheerful, giggly, sad).
6. **Black** is to **white** as **old** is to (borrowed, new, second-hand).
7. **Rich** is to **poor** as **boy** is to (friends, family, girl).
8. **Clean** is to **dirty** as **night** is to (evening, day, afternoon).

■ Underline the word in brackets that is most **opposite** in meaning to the word in capitals.

> **Example** BEFORE (when, then, <u>after</u>, morning, begin)

9. SHOUT (soft, angry, growl, whisper, tell)
10. FRONT (top, back, shed, stripe, garden)
11. SOFT (difficult, fur, nap, bed, hard)

■ Read the following information. Work out the answer. Write your answer on the line.

12. Jay has **10** red cars and **5** blue cars. He gives **6** red cars away and loses **2** blue cars. How many red cars does Jay have left? _____

End of test.

Score:		Time taken:		Target met?	

1–4. For each of the words below, choose the correct group. Write its letter on the line.

W = water creature   **L** = land animal

octopus _____   deer _____   squirrel _____   fox _____

camel _____   whale _____   dolphin _____   salmon _____

In each group, three words go together and one is the odd one out. Underline the word that does **not** go with the other three.

Example pound   <u>coin</u>   hit   thump

5. piano   bow   tambourine   drums

6. sea   river   lake   beach

7. sprint   jog   drive   walk

8. morning   yesterday   afternoon   night

Underline the word that goes best with the three words in brackets.

Example (wet, soaking, moist)   <u>damp</u>, swamp, rotten

9. (biscuit, chocolate, bun)   present, candle, cake

10. (river, lake, ocean)   boat, sea, sand

11. (pupil, headmaster, student)   teacher, book, homework

Read the following information. Work out the answer. Write your answer on the line.

12. Krisztina paints the nails on her left hand with red nail varnish and the nails on her right hand with pink nail varnish. She then paints her toe nails alternating pink and red.
How many nails does she paint red? _____

End of test.

Score:	Time taken:	Target met?

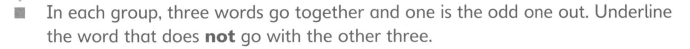

Target time: **12 minutes**

In each group, three words go together and one is the odd one out. Underline the word that does **not** go with the other three.

Example pound   <u>coin</u>   hit   thump

1. mother   niece   aunt   brother
2. feathers   fur   claws   scales
3. dull   exciting   dreary   boring
4. song   melody   story   tune

Choose the word that best completes the sentence. Underline the answer.

Example **Music** is to **listen** as **food** is to (touch, <u>taste</u>, drop).

5. **Quick** is to **fast** as **large** is to (tiny, big, teeny).
6. **Small** is to **little** as **cheerful** is to (jolly, grumpy, pessimistic).
7. **Cold** is to **cool** as **hot** is to (chilly, warm, freezing).
8. **Light** is to **bright** as **dark** is to (day, dim, blazing).

Underline the two words, **one** from each group, that mean almost the **same**.

Example (typical, <u>false</u>, halt)   (unusual, real, <u>untrue</u>)

9. (break, make, bake)   (create, take, lake)
10. (mud, fall, dirty)   (rugby, bathe, filthy)
11. (hope, candle, magic)   (wish, flame, witch)

Circle the letter next to the **true** statement.

12. Libraries have lots of books in them. Libraries lend the books to people.

If the above statements are true, which one of the following statements must also be true?
A. People can borrow books from libraries.
B. Books are very interesting.
C. People of all ages visit libraries.
D. All towns have libraries.

End of test.

Score:	Time taken:	Target met?

Target time: **12 minutes**

■ Add the same letter to each word pair to make two new words. Choose from the letters below. Only use each letter once. Write the two new words on the lines. Put it in the same position in each word.

e o l m g

Example ape, old   ___gape___ , ___gold___   (add **g** to the start of each word)

1. fin, win   _____ , _____

2. lop, hop   _____ , _____

3. sow, bow   _____ , _____

4. tea, sea   _____ , _____

■ In each of the sentences below, the word in capitals has three letters missing. Those three letters spell a word. Write the three-letter word in the gap.

Example My favourite toy is my teddy B E A R.   (EAR)

5. He paid his bus F __ __ __.

6. She flew her red __ __ __ E in the park.

7. The __ __ __ D little girl tidied her room.

8. The story was A B __ __ __ a dragon.

■ Rearrange the word in capitals. Use the letters to make another word that goes with the first two. Write the new word on the line.

Example high up POT ___TOP___

9. coffee milk EAT _____

10. point end PIT _____

11. rod hook TEN _____

■ Read the following information. Work out the answer. Write your answer on the line.

12. I am racing my two friends to school. I arrive at school first. Meg is third to arrive. Reuben arrives at school before Meg. Who arrives second? _____

End of test.

| Score: | | Time taken: | | Target met? | |

Notes for parents, tutors, teachers and other adult helpers

- **Verbal Reasoning 2** is designed for seven- and eight- year-olds, but may also be suitable for some older children.

- Remove this pull-out section before giving the book to the child.

- Before the child begins work on the first test, read together the instructions on page 2, headed **What to do**. As you do so, look together at **Section 1 Test 1** or another of the Section 1 tests and point out to the child the different elements.

- As each question type is introduced for the first time within a particular test, an example is given. Where question types recur throughout the book, the same example is provided. This is deliberate: the example will act as a useful reminder, but children will not need to work through it repeatedly from scratch.

- Make sure that the child understands how to answer the questions and that he or she has a pencil and eraser. You should also ensure that the child is able to see a clock or a watch.

- Be sure that the child knows to tell you clearly when he or she has finished the test.

- When the child is ready, say 'Start the test now' and make a note of the start time.

- When the child has finished, work out how long he or she took to complete the test. Then fill in the **Time taken** box, which appears at the end of the test.

- Mark the child's work using this pull-out section, giving one mark for each correct answer unless instructed otherwise. Then complete the **Score** box at the end of the test.

- The table below shows you how to mark the **Target met?** box and the **Action** notes help you to plan the next step. However, these are suggestions only. Please use your own judgement as you decide how best to proceed.

Score	Time taken*	Target met?	Action
1–6	Any	Not yet	Provide help and support as needed.
7–9	Any	Not yet	Encourage the child to keep practising using the tests in this book. The child may need to repeat some tests. If so, wait a few weeks, or the child may simply remember the correct answers. Provide help and support as needed.
10–12	Over target – child took too long	Not yet	
10–12	On target – child took suggested time or less	Yes	Encourage the child to keep practising using further tests in this book, and to move on to the next book when you think this is appropriate.

- Whatever the test score, always encourage the child to have another go at the questions that he or she got wrong – without looking at the solutions. If the child's answers are still incorrect, work through these questions together. Demonstrate the correct method if necessary.

- If the child struggles with particular question types, help him or her to develop the strategies needed.

Answers

Section 1 Test 1 (page 4)

1. cheerful, joyful
2. damp, wet
3. beat, hit
4. kitchen
5. doctor
6. bark
7. right, left
8. sit, stand
9. clean, dirty
10. green (all colours)
11. car (all vehicles)
12. kangaroo (all animals)

Section 1 Test 2 (page 5)

1–3. *[score half a point for each correct answer]*
    robin = B, tune = F, cuckoo = B, owl = B,
    trout = F, cod = F
4. road (the others are all found in a building)
5. field (the other words are all parts of
    a tree)
6. driver (the others are all forms of transport)
7. quick, slow
8. rich, poor
9. come, go
10. fast is (The train is fast.)
11. see you (How many boats can you see?)
12. milk drink (My cat likes to drink milk.)

Section 1 Test 3 (page 6)

1. smart, clever
2. finish, end
3. slim, thin
4. slow
5. right
6. puppy
7–9. *[score half a point for each correct answer]*
    giraffe = A, duck = B, leopard = A,
    pig = B, elephant = A, goat = B
10. chair (the others are found on plants)
11. giraffe (the others are big cats)
12. dirty (the others are all synonyms of clean)

Section 1 Test 4 (page 7)

1. all, ill (remove first letter)
2. win, tan (remove last letter)
3. ate, own (remove first letter)
4. OLD (GOLD)
5. RIP (STRIPES)
6. ICE (MICE)
7. chair
8. bread
9. bird
10. d (sound and dance)
11. p (damp and plane)
12. g (going and gloat)

Section 1 Test 5 (page 8)

1. alarm   arm
2. float   oat
3. women   men
4. l (trail and lift)
5. h (fresh and haunt)
6. t (treat and teach)
7. not, ton
8. pan, nap
9. net, ten
10. household
11. stepladder
12. blindfold

Section 1 Test 6 (page 9)

1. SUN [BUN] BUG
2. LOG [DOG] DON
3. BUN [BUT] CUT
4. RUB (RUBBER)
5. END (FRIEND)
6. INK (DRINK)
7. toothpaste
8. hairbrush
9. lighthouse
10. two
11. string
12. spanner

Section 1 Test 7 (page 10)

1. **18** (+3)
2. **25** (−10)
3. **24** (+4)
4. **C** (2 + 6 = 8)
5. **D** (3 + 4 = 7)
6. **A** (10 − 9 = 1)
7. **22** (a + b)
8. **50** (a + b)
9. **15** (a + b)
10. **2**
11. **1**
12. **3**

Section 1 Test 8 (page 11)

1. **EE** (+1, +1)
2. **PP** (+1, +1)
3. **VV** (+1, +1)
4. **O** (+2)
5. **T** (+3)
6. **J** (−2)
7. **log**
8. **pin**
9. **old**
10. **851**
11. **156**
12. **CAT**

Section 1 Test 9 (page 12)

1. **73** (a + b)
2. **6** (a − b)
3. **7** (a − b)
4. **10**
5. **3**
6. **54**
7. **20** (+4)
8. **57** (+11)
9. **30** (+5)
10. **C** (6 + 3 = 9)
11. **A** (11 − 4 = 7)
12. **C** (2 × 6 = 12)

Section 1 Test 10 (page 13)

1. **TOP** (−1 from the code to the word)
2. **AIM** (−1 from the code to the word)
3. **MUD** (−3 from the code to the word)
4. **376**
5. **352**
6. **PIPE**
7. **once**
8. **nine**
9. **tuna**
10. **PP** (repeating pattern)
11. **EV** (+1, −1)
12. **JK** (+1, +1)

Section 1 Test 11 (page 14)

1. **his sister**
2. **James**
3. **42**
4. **14**
5. **D**
6. **A**
7. **Thursday**
8. **January**
9. **Saturday**
10. **November**
11. **7**
12. **winter**

Section 1 Test 12 (page 15)

1. **Peep**
2. **A**
3. **9 a.m./nine o'clock/09:00**
4. **6**
5. **9**
6. **7**
7. **1 hour/60 minutes**
8. **1.30 p.m./half past one/13:30**
9. **3.00 p.m./three o'clock/15:00**
10. **11.00 a.m./eleven o'clock/11:00**
11. **1 hour/60 minutes**
12. **5.00 p.m./five o'clock/17:00**

Answers

Section 2 Test 1 (page 16)

1. 5
2. 5
3. 4
4. D
5. D
6. B
7. Wednesday
8. February
9. Saturday
10. September
11. Tuesday
12. summer

Section 2 Test 2 (page 17)

1. gift
2. hurry
3. aid
4. begin
5. sad
6. new
7. girl
8. day
9. whisper
10. back
11. hard
12. 4

Section 2 Test 3 (page 18)

1–4. [score half a point for each correct answer]
octopus = W, deer = L, squirrel = L,
fox = L, camel = L, whale = W,
dolphin = W, salmon = W
5. bow (the rest are musical instruments)
6. beach (the others are all to do with water)
7. drive (this is the only one using a vehicle)
8. yesterday (the others are parts of a day)
9. cake (all baked goods)
10. sea (all large bodies of water)
11. teacher (all people at school)
12. 10

Section 2 Test 4 (page 19)

1. brother (the others are all female relatives)
2. claws (the rest are found on an animal's skin)
3. exciting (the others are synonyms of dull)
4. story (the others are to do with music)
5. big
6. jolly
7. warm
8. dim
9. make, create
10. dirty, filthy
11. hope, wish
12. A

Section 2 Test 5 (page 20)

1. fine, wine (add e)
2. loop, hoop (add o)
3. slow, blow (add l)
4. team, seam (add m)
5. ARE (FARE)
6. KIT (KITE)
7. GOO (GOOD) (accept KIN, KIND)
8. OUT (ABOUT)
9. TEA
10. TIP
11. NET
12. Reuben

Section 2 Test 6 (page 21)

1. car
2. step
3. fireman
4. electricity
5. SEA [SET] GET
6. MOW [SOW] SON
7. BAG [BIG] DIG
8. FAN [BAN] BAP
9. classroom
10. seaweed
11. hummingbird
12. 16

■ Section 2 Test 7 (page 22)

1. li<u>cence</u>   lice
2. leng<u>then</u>   then
3. <u>trapp</u>ed   trap
4. <u>show</u>n   show
5. s (press and shear)
6. d (rapid and dress)
7. e (stole and earn)
8. suitcase
9. lightbulb
10. toothpick
11. armpit
12. 2

■ Section 2 Test 8 (page 23)

1. 66 (+11)
2. 24 (+3)
3. 12 (−5)
4. 60 (+10)
5. D (20 ÷ 10 = 2)
6. A (5 × 3 = 15)
7. A (2 × 5 = 10)
8. B (8 + 9 = 17)
9. 61 (a − b)
10. 0 (a − b)
11. 7 (a ÷ b)
12. pears

■ Section 2 Test 9 (page 24)

1. cat
2. tall
3. win
4. sort
5. 935
6. 394
7. 1993
8. WOOD
9. AR (same, +1)
10. IS (+2, +2)
11. XU (+1, +2, +3, +4)
12. kiwis

■ Section 2 Test 10 (page 25)

1. 50 (a + b)
2. 50 (a + b)
3. 11 (a ÷ b)
4. 12 (a − b)
5. 9
6. 2
7. 1
8. A (28 − 9 = 19)
9. C (100 ÷ 10 = 10)
10. A (18 ÷ 2 = 9)
11. D (9 + 5 = 14)
12. B

■ Section 2 Test 11 (page 26)

1. 5
2. 1
3. 2
4. 1
5. 19 (+4)
6. 12 (−3)
7. 16 (+4)
8. 1 (÷10)
9. C (30 ÷ 5 = 6)
10. D (22 − 8 = 14)
11. D (24 ÷ 2 = 12)
12. Friday

■ Section 2 Test 12 (page 27)

1. keep
2. king
3. mile
4. dent
5. NEW (−1 from the code to the word)
6. LCY (+2 from the word to the code)
7. MBC (+1 from the word to the code)
8. OLH (+3 from the word to the code)
9. V (+3)
10. D (−3)
11. G (+5)
12. 7

Answers

■ Section 3 Test 1 (page 28)

1–4. *[score half a point for each correct answer]*
hood = H, slipper = F, helmet = H, bonnet = H, sandal = F, cap = H, trainer = F, boot = F
5. **16** (+2)
6. **22** (–11)
7. **16** (×2)
8. **51** (–10)
9. staircase
10. graveyard
11. woodland
12. **2**

■ Section 3 Test 2 (page 29)

1. **3** (a ÷ b)
2. **30** (a + b)
3. **12** (a × b)
4. **21** (a – b)
5. BUS
6. CUT
7. TON
8. NAP
9. HEN (WHEN)
10. HER (OTHER)
11. BIT (BITE)
12. A

■ Section 3 Test 3 (page 30)

1. sea, pea (remove last letter)
2. cut, hut (remove third letter)
3. tap, fat (remove second letter)
4. lot, low (remove first letter)
5. 2
6. 8
7. 6
8. 4
9. 415
10. 724
11. POOL
12. Beth

■ Section 3 Test 4 (page 31)

1. mule
2. daft
3. cousin
4. sell
5. **M** (–5)
6. **NO** (+2, +2)
7. **EG** (+3, +3)
8. **TU** (+1, +1)
9. **A** (5 × 9 = 45)
10. **B** (18 + 12 = 30)
11. **D** (60 ÷ 10 = 6)
12. **16**

■ Section 3 Test 5 (page 32)

1. **the feeds** (The zookeeper feeds the elephants.)
2. **my is** (Here is my house.)
3. **the watched** (The boy watched the match.)
4. **dresses wear** (Girls often wear dresses.)
5. **c** (music and chalk)
6. **f** (sniff and fudge)
7. **e** (dodge and early)
8. **l** (snarl and lever)
9. **VG** (–1, –1)
10. **IH** (+2, same)
11. **SS** (repeating pattern)
12. Anya

■ Section 3 Test 6 (page 33)

1. **D** (5 × 8 = 40)
2. **C** (24 – 12 = 12)
3. **B** (11 × 2 = 22)
4. **A** (25 ÷ 5 = 5)
5. **BAR** (–2 from the code to the word)
6. **LMU** (–2 from the word to the code)
7. **GJY** (+1 from the word to the code)
8. love, adore
9. happy, glad
10. tasty, delicious
11. munch, chew
12. **5**

Section 3 Test 7 (page 34)

1. waterfall
2. rainbow
3. farmyard
4. k (spook and king)
5. d (greed and dined)
6. p (group and plant)
7. n (drain and near)
8. imprint imp
9. shell she
10. neighbour our
11. shipped hip
12. 4 May

Section 3 Test 8 (page 35)

1. 60 (a × b)
2. 4 (a ÷ b)
3. 23 (a + b)
4. 12 (a − b)
5. best, worst
6. lift, drop
7. throw, catch
8. same, different
9. GAS [GAP] RAP
10. BOAT [MOAT] MOAN
11. FLIP [SLIP] SLIM
12. D

Section 3 Test 9 (page 36)

1. gain
2. nap
3. drop
4. pun
5. terrifying (all synonyms for frightening)
6. glass (all types of materials)
7. smell (all senses)
8. right (all directions)
9. nice
10. sort
11. well
12. Raj's shop

Section 3 Test 10 (page 37)

1. BC (−2, −2)
2. UW (+3, +3)
3. DE (+2, +2)
4. NL (+3, +3)
5. clothes (the others are types of furniture)
6. glove (the others are types of footwear)
7. whisper (the others are loud noises)
8. WT (same, +1)
9. OK (+2, −3)
10. QK (−1, −1)
11. NO (+3, +3)
12. Yes

Section 3 Test 11 (page 38)

1. rabbit
2. aunt
3. slither
4. rich
5. 10 (−5)
6. 9 (+2)
7. 3 (÷2)
8. 21 (+4)
9. sent
10. fire
11. rage
12. 30 minutes/half an hour

Section 3 Test 12 (page 39)

1. 9
2. 10
3. 10
4. 6
5. 715
6. 7519
7. AJAR
8. run, walk
9. laugh, cry
10. break, fix
11. stay, leave
12. C

This book of answers is a pull-out section from
Rapid Reasoning Tests: Verbal Reasoning 2

Published by Schofield & Sims Ltd,
Dogley Mill, Fenay Bridge, Huddersfield HD8 0NQ, UK
Telephone 01484 607080
www.schofieldandsims.co.uk

Copyright © Schofield & Sims Ltd, 2014

Author: Siân Goodspeed. Siân Goodspeed has asserted her moral right under the Copyright, Designs and Patents Act, 1988, to be identified as the author of this work.

British Library Cataloguing in Publication Data. A catalogue record for this book is available from the British Library.

Commissioned by **Carolyn Richardson Publishing Services** (www.publiserve.co.uk)

Design by **Oxford Designers & Illustrators**
Printed in India by **Multivista Global Ltd**

ISBN 978 07217 1239 0

Target time: 12 minutes

■ If these words were listed in alphabetical order, which word would come **third**? Write the answer on the line.

Example water   juice   milk   cup   jug   ___juice___

1. car   van   lorry   boat   barge   _____

2. walk   run   waddle   jog   step   _____

3. farmer   grocer   fireman   doctor   nurse   _____

4. air   water   fire   earth   electricity   _____

■ Change the first word into the last word. Only change **one** letter at a time. You must make a new word in the middle. Write the new word on the line.

Example SIN [___BIN___] BIG

5. SEA [_____] GET

6. MOW [_____] SON

7. BAG [_____] DIG

8. FAN [_____] BAP

■ Underline the two words, **one** from each group, that together make one new word. The word from the first group comes first.

Example (<u>basket</u>, bag, shop)   (pin, <u>ball</u>, bin)   (basketball)

9. (class, rules, teacher)   (school, pupil, room)

10. (beach, sea, sand)   (wave, weed, flag)

11. (singing, humming, crying)   (fish, mouse, bird)

■ Read the following information. Work out the answer. Write your answer on the line.

12. Nisha plays tennis on Saturdays. In the morning she has 14 tennis balls.
She loses 3 balls. Her friend gives her 5 balls.
How many tennis balls does Nisha have at the end of the day? _____

End of test.

Score:		Time taken:		Target met?	

■ Find the **four-letter word** hidden in each longer word. You will not need to change the letter order. Underline the word and write it on the line.

> **Example** tr<u>ain</u>   _____rain_____

1. licence   _____

2. lengthen   _____

3. trapped   _____

4. shown   _____

■ Find the missing letter that completes **both** words. Write the letter on the line. Choose your answer from these letters:

a d m s e f

> **Example** bea (_m_) atch   (beam and match)

5. pres (__) hear

6. rapi (__) ress

7. stol (__) arn

■ Underline the two words, **one** from each group, that together make one new word. The word from the first group comes first.

> **Example** (<u>basket</u>, bag, shop)   (pin, <u>ball</u>, bin)   (basketball)

8. (suit, tie, jacket)   (file, case, link)

9. (light, move, hose)   (bulb, flower, pot)

10. (teeth, tooth, mouth)   (scratch, bite, pick)

11. (body, leg, arm)   (mine, pit, shirt)

■ Read the following information. Work out the answer. Write your answer on the line.

12. Frank's friends are called Bill, Rebecca, Bryony and Amir. Frank's father is called Brian. How many of Frank's friends have a name beginning with B? _____

End of test.

Score:	Time taken:	Target met?

Target time: **12 minutes**

■ Find the next number in the sequence. Write it on the line.

| **Example** | 18 | 16 | 14 | 12 | 10 | ___8___ | (–2 each time) |

1. 22   33   44   55   _____

2. 12   15   18   21   _____

3. 32   27   22   17   _____

4. 20   30   40   50   _____

....

■ Use the information given to answer the sum. Write your answer as a **letter**.

| **Example** | A = 2 | B = 4 | C = 5 | D = 6 | **A + B =** ___D___ | (2 + 4 = 6) |

5. A = 20   B = 10   C = 25   D = 2   **A ÷ B =** _____

6. A = 15   B = 10   C = 3   D = 5   **D × C =** _____

7. A = 10   B = 2   C = 17   D = 5   **B × D =** _____

8. A = 8   B = 17   C = 19   D = 9   **A + D =** _____

....

■ Work out the missing number. Write it on the line.

Example 5 [9] 4   2 [5] 3   7 [___10___] 3
(a + b = ?, where a is the number on the left and b is the number on the right)

9. 14 [8] 6   59 [49] 10   77 [_____] 16

10. 63 [50] 13   24 [17] 7   8 [_____] 8

11. 80 [8] 10   90 [9] 10   70 [_____] 10

....

■ Read the following information. Work out the answer. Write your answer on the line.

12. My mother buys some apples, bananas and pears. She buys the bananas after she buys the pears, but before she buys the apples.
Which did she buy first: apples, bananas or pears? _____

End of test.

| Score: | | Time taken: | | Target met? | |

Target time: **12 minutes**

■ Make a new word. Change the third pair of words in the same way as the other pairs. Write the new word on the line.

> **Example** (bank, ban) (cool, coo) (dent, _____den_____)
> (take away the last letter of the first word)

1. (knit, kit) (snip, sip) (coat, _____)

2. (learn, earn) (steam, team) (stall, _____)

3. (town, tow) (took, too) (wing, _____)

4. (stack, sack) (smock, sock) (snort, _____)

■ Match the number codes to the words. Use this to help you work out the answers to the questions. Write your answers on the lines.

> OWL   OUT   DUO   529   913   924

5. What is the code for **OLD**? _____

6. What is the code for **LOT**? _____

7. What is the code for **WOOL**? _____

8. What does the code **1995** mean? _____

■ Find the next letter pair in the sequence. Use the alphabet to help you. Write your answer on the line.

A B C D E F G H I J K L M N O P Q R S T U V W X Y Z

> **Example** AB   BC   CD   DE   EF   _FG_   (+1, +1)

9. AN AO AP AQ _____

10. AK CM EO GQ _____

11. NK OL QN TQ _____

■ Read the following information. Work out the answer. Write your answer on the line.

12. Jenny only likes red fruits. Josef only likes yellow and orange fruits. They share a fruit salad that is made of strawberries, oranges, bananas, kiwis, pineapple and cherries.
Which of the fruits in the salad do neither of them eat? _____

End of test.

Score:	Time taken:	Target met?

Target time: 12 minutes

■ Work out the missing number. Write it on the line.

> **Example** 5 [9] 4   2 [5] 3   7 [__10__] 3
> (a + b = ?, where a is the number on the left and b is the number on the right)

1. 20 [50] 30   10 [50] 40   15 [_____] 35
2. 49 [50] 1   48 [50] 2   47 [_____] 3
3. 15 [3] 5   25 [5] 5   55 [_____] 5
4. 19 [10] 9   18 [9] 9   21 [_____] 9

■ Find the missing number in each equation. Write it on the line.

> **Example** 3 + 3 = 4 + __2__   (3 + 3 = 6 and so does 4 + 2)

5. 24 – 6 = 2 × _____
6. 60 ÷ 5 = 6 × _____
7. 7 × 2 = 13 + _____

■ Use the information given to answer the sum. Write your answer as a **letter**.

> **Example** A = 2   B = 4   C = 5   D = 6   **A + B =** __D__   (2 + 4 = 6)

8. A = 19   B = 28   C = 36   D = 9   **B – D =** _____
9. A = 20   B = 100   C = 10   D = 5   **B ÷ C =** _____
10. A = 9   B = 2   C = 22   D = 18   **D ÷ B =** _____
11. A = 9   B = 5   C = 21   D = 14   **A + B =** _____

■ Circle the letter next to the **true** statement.

12. Father always wears his glasses to read books. Father is reading a book now.

   If the above statements are true, which one of the following statements must also be true?
   A. Reading books is bad for your eyes.
   B. Father is wearing his glasses now.
   C. The television is boring.
   D. Father needs to clean his glasses.

End of test.

Score:		Time taken:		Target met?	

■ Find the missing number in each equation. Write it on the line.

Example $3 + 3 = 4 +$ ___2___ $(3 + 3 = 6 \text{ and so does } 4 + 2)$

1. $5 \times 5 = 20 +$ _____

2. $7 \times 5 = 36 -$ _____

3. $50 \div 10 = 3 +$ _____

4. $20 \div 5 = 3 +$ _____

■ Find the next number in the sequence. Write it on the line.

Example 18   16   14   12   10   ___8___   (−2 each time)

5. 3   7   11   15   _____

6. 24   21   18   15   _____

7. 0   4   8   12   _____

8. 10000   1000   100   10   _____

■ Use the information given to answer the sum. Write your answer as a **letter**.

Example $A = 2$ $B = 4$ $C = 5$ $D = 6$ **$A + B =$** ___D___ $(2 + 4 = 6)$

9. $A = 30$ $B = 5$ $C = 6$ $D = 40$ **$A \div B =$** _____

10. $A = 8$ $B = 22$ $C = 32$ $D = 14$ **$B - A =$** _____

11. $A = 30$ $B = 2$ $C = 24$ $D = 12$ **$C \div B =$** _____

■ Read the following question. Work out the answer. Write your answer on the line.

12. What is the day after Thursday? _____

End of test.

Score:	Time taken:	Target met?

Target time: **12 minutes**

The word in square brackets has been made by some of the letters from the two outside words. Make a new word in the middle of the second group of words in the same way. Write the new word on the line.

Example (left [lead] read)   (jogs [____joke____] pike)

1. (bride [desk] skip)   (stake [_____] epic)
2. (slat [slug] smug)   (kite [_____] hung)
3. (hilt [hire] reap)   (mint [_____] left)
4. (west [word] cord)   (dice [_____] rent)

Find the code. Use the alphabet to help you. Write your answer on the line.
A B C D E F G H I J K L M N O P Q R S T U V W X Y Z

Example If the code for **FIT** is **GJU**, what is the code for **WAD**?   XBE
(+1 from the word to the code)

5. If the code **BOU** means **ANT**, what does the code **OFX** mean? _____
6. If the code for **BED** is **DGF**, what is the code for **JAW**? _____
7. If the code for **HOT** is **IPU**, what is the code for **LAB**? _____
8. If the code for **BOW** is **ERZ**, what is the code for **LIE**? _____

Find the letter that completes each sentence. Use the alphabet to help you. Write your answer on the line.
A B C D E F G H I J K L M N O P Q R S T U V W X Y Z

Example **C** is to **D** as **E** is to __F__ .   (+1)

9. **V** is to **Y** as **S** is to _____ .
10. **Q** is to **N** as **G** is to _____ .
11. **H** is to **M** as **B** is to _____ .

Read the following information. Work out the answer. Write your answer on the line.

12. Chen is 14. Her brother is half her age. How old is Chen's brother? _____

End of test.

Score:		Time taken:		Target met?	

Section **3** Test **1**

■ **1–4.** For each of the words below, choose the correct group. Write its letter on the line.

F = foot   **H** = head

hood _____   slipper _____   helmet _____   bonnet _____

sandal _____   cap _____   trainer _____   boot _____

....

■ Find the next number in the sequence. Write it on the line.

Example 18   16   14   12   10   __8__   (−2 each time)

5. 8   10   12   14   _____

6. 66   55   44   33   _____

7. 1   2   4   8   _____

8. 91   81   71   61   _____

....

■ Underline the two words, **one** from each group, that together make one new word. The word from the first group comes first.

Example (<u>basket</u>, bag, shop)   (pin, <u>ball</u>, bin)   (basketball)

9. (step, climb, stair)   (file, case, need)

10. (grave, serious, mood)   (garden, yard, church)

11. (forest, wood, tree)   (land, country, place)

....

■ Read the following information. Work out the answer. Write your answer on the line.

12. Patrick has 3 pet parrots. One has blue, red and yellow feathers. One has green, yellow and blue feathers. The last parrot has red, blue and green feathers.
How many parrots have red feathers? _____

End of test.

| Score: | | Time taken: | | Target met? | |

Work out the missing number. Write it on the line.

Example 5 [9] 4   2 [5] 3   7 [___10___] 3
(a + b = ?, where a is the number on the left and b is the number on the right)

1. 45 [9] 5   55 [11] 5   15 [_____] 5

2. 12 [23] 11   15 [40] 25   17 [_____] 13

3. 4 [8] 2   2 [4] 2   6 [_____] 2

4. 22 [19] 3   35 [30] 5   27 [_____] 6

Rearrange the capital letters to make a new word so that the sentence makes sense. Write the new word on the line.

Example The **NMA** put on his hat. ____MAN____

5. Gran caught the USB. _____

6. Dad TUC the lawn. _____

7. The elephant weighed a NOT. _____

8. The dog curled up for a PNA. _____

In each of the sentences below, the word in capitals has three letters missing. Those three letters spell a word. Write the three-letter word in the gap.

Example My favourite toy is my teddy B E A R. (EAR)

9. W __ __ __ are we going?

10. Where is my O T __ __ __ shoe?

11. Be careful, the dog might __ __ __ E you!

Circle the letter next to the **true** statement.

12. Rock pools are found at the seaside. Crabs live in rock pools.

If the above statements are true, which one of the following statements must also be true?

A. Crabs are found at the seaside.   C. Seaweed grows on rocks.
B. There is a lot of sand on a beach.   D. Crabs walk sideways.

End of test.

Score:	Time taken:	Target met?

■ Take a letter away from each word to make two new words. The letter you take away should be in the same position in each word in the pair.

Example chat, film   ____cat____, ____fan____   (remove the second letter from each word)

1. seal, peal   _____, _____

2. curt, hurt   _____, _____

3. trap, flat   _____, _____

4. clot, flow   _____, _____

....

■ Find the missing number in each equation. Write it on the line.

Example $3 + 3 = 4 +$ ____2____ $(3 + 3 = 6$ and so does $4 + 2)$

5. $80 ÷ 10 = 4 ×$ _____

6. $7 × 4 = 20 +$ _____

7. $2 × 12 = 18 +$ _____

8. $50 ÷ 5 = 14 -$ _____

....

■ Match the number codes to the words. Use this to help you work out the answers to the questions. Write your answers on the lines.

DOG   GAP   LAD   324   513   725

9. What is the code for **POD**? _____

10. What is the code for **LAP**? _____

11. What does the code **4117** mean? _____

....

■ Read the following information. Work out the answer. Write your answer on the line.

12. Seona is driving a car. Grace is sitting on Seona's left. Jill is sitting behind Seona.
Beth is sitting behind Grace.
Who is sitting on Jill's left? _____

End of test.

Score:		Time taken:		Target met?	

Target time: **12 minutes**

■ If these words were listed in alphabetical order, which word would come **third**? Write the answer on the line.

Example water   juice   milk   cup   jug   ___juice___

1. zebra   horse   pony   donkey   mule   _____

2. kind   clever   cruel   daft   friendly   _____

3. uncle   aunt   cousin   brother   daughter   _____

4. market   shop   stall   buy   sell   _____

■ Find the letter or letter pair that completes each sentence. Use the alphabet to help you. Write your answer on the line.

A B C D E F G H I J K L M N O P Q R S T U V W X Y Z

Example **CE** is to **DF** as **EG** is to ___FH___.   (+1, +1)

5. **X** is to **S** as **R** is to _____ .

6. **CD** is to **EF** as **LM** is to _____ .

7. **DF** is to **GI** as **BD** is to _____ .

8. **OP** is to **PQ** as **ST** is to _____ .

■ Use the information given to answer the sum. Write your answer as a **letter**.

Example A = 2   B = 4   C = 5   D = 6   **A + B =** ___D___   (2 + 4 = 6)

9. A = 45   B = 5   C = 80   D = 9   **B × D =** _____

10. A = 12   B = 30   C = 20   D = 18   **D + A =** _____

11. A = 50   B = 10   C = 60   D = 6   **C ÷ B =** _____

■ Read the following information. Work out the answer. Write your answer on the line.

12. Jess and Abdul are bird-watching. Jess sees 2 pigeons, 3 doves and a robin. Abdul sees 7 sparrows and 3 blackbirds. How many birds do Jess and Abdul spot altogether? _____

End of test.

Score:		Time taken:		Target met?	

■ **Two** words in each sentence must change places so that the sentence makes sense. Underline the words.

> **Example** I a need nap.   (I need a nap.)

1. The zookeeper the feeds elephants.

2. Here my is house.

3. The boy the watched match.

4. Girls often dresses wear.

■ Find the missing letter that completes **both** words. Write the letter on the line. Choose your answer from these letters:

j e f c l m

> **Example** bea (_m_) atch   (beam and match)

5. musi (__) halk

6. snif (__) udge

7. dodg (__) arly

8. snar (__) ever

■ Find the next letter pair in the sequence. Use the alphabet to help you. Write your answer on the line.

A B C D E F G H I J K L M N O P Q R S T U V W X Y Z

> **Example** AB   BC   CD   DE   EF   _FG_   (+1, +1)

9. ZK YJ XI WH _____

10. AH CH EH GH _____

11. SS TT SS TT _____

■ Read the following information. Work out the answer. Write your answer on the line.

12. Four children are waiting in the line for the ice-cream van. James is second in the line. Miles is at the back of the line. Anya is in front of Miles. Ayesha is at the front of the line. Who is third in the line? _____

End of test.

Score:		Time taken:		Target met?	

Target time: 12 minutes

■ Use the information given to answer the sum. Write your answer as a **letter**.

> **Example** A = 2   B = 4   C = 5   D = 6   **A + B =** ___D___   (2 + 4 = 6)

1. A = 5   B = 60   C = 8   D = 40   **A × C =** _____

2. A = 24   B = 30   C = 12   D = 2   **A − C =** _____

3. A = 2   B = 22   C = 11   D = 20   **C × A =** _____

4. A = 5   B = 30   C = 15   D = 25   **D ÷ A =** _____

■ Find the code. Use the alphabet to help you. Write your answer on the line.

A B C D E F G H I J K L M N O P Q R S T U V W X Y Z

> **Example** If the code for **FIT** is **GJU**, what is the code for **WAD**?   ___XBE___
>
> (+1 from the word to the code)

5. If the code for **AXE** is **CZG**, what does the code **DCT** mean? _____

6. If **ICE** is written in code as **GAC**, what is the code for **NOW**? _____

7. If the code for **GAP** is **HBQ**, what is the code for **FIX**? _____

■ Underline the pair of words that mean almost the **same**.

> **Example** (typical, unusual)   (halt, real)   (false, untrue)

8. (heart, kiss)   (love, adore)   (dine, card)

9. (happy, glad)   (smile, trick)   (dream, nap)

10. (meal, aroma)   (stir, cook)   (tasty, delicious)

11. (swallow, squeeze)   (spit, rude)   (munch, chew)

■ Read the following information. Work out the answer. Write your answer on the line.

12. Nathan does the washing-up every day except Friday. On Mondays and Wednesdays he wears pink rubber gloves. On Tuesdays, Thursdays and Saturdays he wears blue rubber gloves. On Sundays he doesn't wear any gloves.
On how many days of the week does Nathan wear gloves to do the washing-up?

_____

End of test.

Score:		Time taken:		Target met?	

Target time: **12 minutes**

■ Underline the two words, **one** from each group, that together make one new word. The word from the first group comes first.

> **Example** (<u>basket</u>, bag, shop)　(pin, <u>ball</u>, bin)　(basketball)

1. (river, rush, water)　(flow, fall, drop)

2. (rain, lake, cloud)　(arrow, bow, shoot)

3. (farm, man, bird)　(place, chair, yard)

■ Find the missing letter that completes **both** words. Write the letter on the line. Choose your answer from these letters:

d k n p c m

> **Example** bea (_m_) atch　(beam and match)

4. spoo (__) ing

5. gree (__) ined

6. grou (__) lant

7. drai (__) ear

■ Find the **three-letter word** hidden in each longer word. You will not need to change the letter order. Underline the word and write it on the line.

> **Example** s<u>too</u>p　　too

8. imprint _____

9. shell _____

10. neighbour _____

11. shipped _____

■ Read the following question. Work out the answer. Write your answer on the line.

12. If it is **3 May** today, what will the date be tomorrow? _____

End of test.

Score:		Time taken:		Target met?	

Target time: **12 minutes**

■ Work out the missing number. Write it on the line.

Example 5 [9] 4   2 [5] 3   7 [_10_] 3
(a + b = ?, where a is the number on the left and b is the number on the right)

1. 2 [10] 5   4 [20] 5   12 [_____] 5

2. 50 [5] 10   60 [6] 10   40 [_____] 10

3. 16 [21] 5   10 [20] 10   14 [_____] 9

4. 17 [8] 9   8 [5] 3   24 [_____] 12

■ Underline the two words, **one** from each group, that are most **opposite** in meaning.

Example (after, morning, begin)   (before, then, when)

5. (naughty, lost, best)   (bad, worst, prize)

6. (through, lift, give)   (drop, slide, bat)

7. (net, throw, hit)   (trick, ball, catch)

8. (same, some, nice)   (like, different, too)

■ Change the first word into the last word. Only change **one** letter at a time. You must make a new word in the middle. Write the new word on the line.

Example SIN [_BIN_] BIG

9. GAS [_____] RAP

10. BOAT [_____] MOAN

11. FLIP [_____] SLIM

■ Circle the letter next to the **true** statement.

12. Ostriches and penguins are birds. Ostriches and penguins cannot fly.

If the above statements are true, which one of the following statements must also be true?
A. Ostriches lay eggs.
B. Penguins are friendly with other birds.
C. Ostriches come from Africa.
D. Not all birds are able to fly.

End of test.

Score:		Time taken:		Target met?	

■ Make a new word. Change the third pair of words in the same way as the other pairs. Write the new word on the line.

Example (bank, ban) (cool, coo) (dent, ___den___)
(remove the last letter of the first word)

1. (sling, sing)   (skill, sill)   (grain, _____)
2. (skip, kip)   (what, hat)   (snap, _____)
3. (cheat, chat)   (cheap, chap)   (droop, _____)
4. (till, ill)   (heel, eel)   (spun, _____)

■ Underline the word that goes best with the three words in brackets.

Example (wet, soaking, moist)   <u>damp</u>, swamp, rotten

5. (frightening, scary, petrifying)   terrifying, boring, silly
6. (paper, plastic, brick)   drain, glass, salt
7. (listen, taste, touch)   cheese, music, smell
8. (up, down, left)   write, right, forgot

■ Choose the word that best completes the sentence. Underline the answer.

Example **Music** is to **listen** as **food** is to (touch, <u>taste</u>, drop).

9. **Mean** is to **nasty** as **kind** is to (arrogant, smiley, nice).
10. **Beautiful** is to **pretty** as **organise** is to (type, sort, play).
11. **Sick** is to **ill** as **healthy** is to (poorly, sad, well).

■ Read the following information. Work out the answer. Write your answer on the line.

12. Raj works in a shop. He sells chocolate bars, magazines and pens.
Leah works in a different shop. She sells cakes, flowers and sweets.
Bella wants to buy a pen. Whose shop must she go to? _____

End of test.

Score:		Time taken:		Target met?	

Target time: **12 minutes**

Find the letter pair that completes each sentence. Use the alphabet to help you. Write your answer on the line.

A B C D E F G H I J K L M N O P Q R S T U V W X Y Z

Example **CE** is to **DF** as **EG** is to ___FH___ .   (+1, +1)

1. **QR** is to **OP** as **DE** is to _____ .
2. **JL** is to **MO** as **RT** is to _____ .
3. **VW** is to **XY** as **BC** is to _____ .
4. **SQ** is to **VT** as **KI** is to _____ .

In each group, three words go together and one is the odd one out. Underline the word that does **not** go with the other three.

Example pound   coin   hit   thump

5. shelf   clothes   cupboard   wardrobe
6. boot   slipper   glove   sandal
7. shout   whisper   scream   yell

Find the next letter pair in the sequence. Use the alphabet to help you. Write your answer on the line.

A B C D E F G H I J K L M N O P Q R S T U V W X Y Z

Example AB   BC   CD   DE   EF   ___FG___   (+1, +1)

8. WP   WQ   WR   WS   _____
9. GW   IT   KQ   MN   _____
10. UO   TN   SM   RL   _____
11. BC   EF   HI   KL   _____

Read the following information. Work out the answer. Write your answer on the line.

12. Liam is counting his money. He has three **20** pence pieces and two **50** pence pieces. Does he have enough money to buy an ice-cream for £1.50? _____

End of test.

Score:		Time taken:		Target met?	

■ Choose the word that best completes the sentence. Underline the answer.

> **Example** **Music** is to **listen** as **food** is to (touch, <u>taste</u>, drop).

1. **House** is to **people** as **hutch** is to (straw, horse, rabbit).
2. **King** is to **queen** as **uncle** is to (brother, aunt, sister).
3. **Leopard** is to **run** as **snake** is to (hop, slither, skip).
4. **Like** is to **dislike** as **poor** is to (rich, unwell, bucket).

■ Find the next number in the sequence. Write it on the line.

> **Example** 18 16 14 12 10 <u>8</u> (–2 each time)

5. 30 25 20 15 _____
6. 1 3 5 7 _____
7. 48 24 12 6 _____
8. 5 9 13 17 _____

■ The word in square brackets has been made by some of the letters from the two outside words. Make a new word in the middle of the second group of words in the same way. Write the new word on the line.

> **Example** (left [lead] read)   (jogs [__<u>joke</u>__] pike)

9. (game [gale] bale)   (seek [_____] font)
10. (fold [four] sure)   (fins [_____] bred)
11. (spit [pink] bunk)   (brat [_____] edge)

■ Read the following information. Work out the answer. Write your answer on the line.

12. Leon starts cooking his dinner at **7.00** p.m. He sits down to eat at **7.30** p.m. How long did it take him to cook his dinner? _____

End of test.

Score: _____ Time taken: _____ Target met? _____